DATE DUE

| | | | |
|---|---|---|---|
| MONTA F | 2 | 6 '76 | |
| GAZ | C 1 0 1 | 7 '78 | |
| | | | |
| | | | |
| | | | |
| | | | |
| | | | |
| | | | |
| | | | |
| | | | |
| | | | |

# ONE'S NONE

## Old Rhymes for New Tongues

# About This Book

Traditional rhymes, songs and catches should be part of every child's literary heritage. Many of them when read aloud to the young child remain with him for ever and become the foundation of a lasting affection for poetry.

James Reeves, leading poet and anthologist, has made a special study of folk ballads and rhymes. This unconventional choice will appeal to the children themselves and to the adults who read to them, not only for the vigour and freshness of the verses but as a change from the more familiar collections.

# ONE'S NONE

## Old Rhymes for New Tongues

*Chosen and arranged by*

*JAMES REEVES*

*Pictures by*

*BERNADETTE WATTS*

watts
*international*

FRANKLIN WATTS, INC.
575 Lexington Avenue,
New York, New York 10022

First Published in Great Britain 1968
by William Heinemann Ltd

First American Publication 1969
by Franklin Watts, Inc.

Library of Congress Catalog Card Number: 68-16779

Printed in Great Britain

# And If You

And if you do buy this book,
Be sure that you do on it look.
Read it over, and you will say
Your money is not thrown away.

# Contents

# One's None

One's none,
Two's some,
Three's a many,
Four's a penny,
Five is a little hundred.

# Birds on a Stone

There were two birds
   Sat on a stone.
One flew away,
   Then there was one.
The other flew after,
   Then there was none,
And so the poor stone
Was left all alone.

14

# The Merry-Ma-Tanza

Here we go round by jingo-ring,
Jingo-ring and jingo-ring,
Here we go round by jingo-ring
About the merry-ma-tanza.

# Green Grass

A-dis, a-dis, a green grass,
  A-dis, a-dis, a-dis,
Come all you pretty fair maids
  And dance along with us.

We will give you pots and pans,
  We will give you brass,
We will give you anything
  For a bonny lass.

We will give you gold and silver,
  We will give you pearl,
We will give you anything
  For a pretty girl.

16

You shall have a duck, my dear,
   And you shall have a dragon,
And you shall have a nice young man
   To dance ere you're forsaken.

You shall have a goose for dinner,
   You shall have a darling,
You shall have a nice young man
   To take you up the garden.

Suppose this young man was to die
   And leave this girl a widow?
The bells would ring, the birds would sing,
   So we'll all clap together.


# Turn, Cheeses, Turn


Green cheeses, yellow laces,
Up and down the market places.
First a penny and then a groat,
Turn, cheeses, turn.

# The Gabelory Man

*(Three versions)*

I

Follow my gabelory man,
Follow my gabelory man.
I'll do all that ever I can
To follow my gabelory man.

We'll borrow a horse and steal a gig,
And round the world we'll have a jig,
And I'll do all that ever I can
To follow my gabelory man.

2

Holy Gabriel, holy man,
Rantum roarum reeden man,
I'll do all that ever I can
To follow my Gabriel, holy man.

3

I sell my bat, I sell my ball,
I sell my spinning wheel and all,
And I'll do all that ever I can
To follow the eyes of the drummer man.

*(Sometimes this rhyme is about the "gaberlunzie man".*
*"Gabelory" is said to mean "gable 'oary (hoary)",*
*meaning a little old man who sits on the gable of*
*every house and brings luck. The words are*
*those of a "follow my leader" game.)*

# Rules of Contrary

Here I go round
   The rules of contrary,
Hopping about
   Like a little canary.
When I say Hold fast,
   Leave go:
When I say Leave go,
   Hold fast.

# Hie Hie

## Hie, Hie

Hie, hie, says Anthony,
Puss in the pantry
Gnawing gnawing
A mutton mutton-bone.
See how she tumbles it,
See how she mumbles it,
See how she tosses
The mutton mutton-bone.

# Rats and Mice

Pretty John Watts,
We are troubled with rats,
Will you drive them out of the house?
We have mice too in plenty
That feast in the pantry,
But let them stay
And nibble away.
What harm is a little brown mouse?

24

# The White Dove

The white dove sat on the castle wall.
I bend my bow, and shoot her I shall.
I put her in my glove, both feathers and all.
I laid my bridle upon the shelf—
If you want any more, sing it yourself.

# What the Cock and Hen Say

"Lock the dairy door!
Lock the dairy door!"

"Chickle, chackle, chee!
I haven't got the key."

# Chicken Come Clock

Chicken come clock around the rock,
Looram, lorram, lumber lock.
Five mile and one o'clock,
   Now the thief is coming.
In comes Tod with his long rod,
And vanishes all from victim Vad.
It is, it was, it must be done,
Tiddlum, toddlum, twenty-one.
The crow's awake, the kite's asleep,
It's time for my poor chickens
To get a bit of something to eat—
   What time is it, old granny?

# Grey Goose and Gander

Grey goose and gander,
Waft your wings together.
Carry the good king's daughter
Over the one-strand river.

# John Cook's Mare

John Cook had a little grey mare,
   He, haw, hum!
Her back stood up and her bones they were bare,
   He, haw, hum!

John Cook was riding up Shuter's Bank,
   He, haw, hum!
And there his nag did kick and prank,
   He, haw, hum!

John Cook was riding up Shuter's Hill,
   He, haw, hum!
His mare fell down and she made her will,
   He, haw, hum!

The bridle and saddle were laid on the shelf,
   He, haw, hum!
If you want any more you may sing it yourself,
   He, haw, hum!

# A-Hunting We Will Go

O have you seen the Shah,
O have you seen the Shah?
　He lights his pipe
　On a starlight night,
O have you seen the Shah?

For a-hunting we will go,
A-hunting we will go.
　We'll catch a fox
　And put him in a box,
And a-hunting we will go.

# One-Eyed Gunner

There was a little one-eyed gunner
Killed all the birds that died last summer.

# Johnny Armstrong

Johnny Armstrong killed a calf,
Peter Henderson got the half,
Willie Wilkinson got the head.
Ring the bell—the calf is dead.

# Colly My Cow

Little Tog Dogget,
  What dost thou mean
To kill my poor Colly
  Now she's so lean?
The skin of my Colly
  Was softer than silk,
And three times a day
  My cow would give milk.

  Sing, O poor Colly,
    Colly, my cow,
  For Colly will give me
    No more milk now.

She every year
  A fine calf did me bring,
Which fetched me a pound,
  For it came in the spring.
But now I have killed her
  I can't her recall.
I will sell my poor Colly,
  Hide, horns and all.

  Sing, O poor Colly,
    Colly, my cow,
  For Colly will give me
    No more milk now.

# The Spider

It was one summer's morning
   As I lay on my bed,
I spied an ancient spider
   A-spinning of her thread.

She wove it in a sunny beam
   As clear as glass could be.
The oldest nun that ever spun
   Ne'er spun so fine as she.

The first that came into the net,
   A silly fly, was slain.
The next that came, a hornet bold,
   Soon broke the net in twain.

And so I often wonder why
   Are poor men brought to shame,
While rich men live in vanity
   And all men praise their name.

# Winter's Thunder

# Winter's Thunder

Winter's thunder
Is the world's wonder.

# The Mackerel's Cry

The mackerel's cry
Is "Never long dry!"

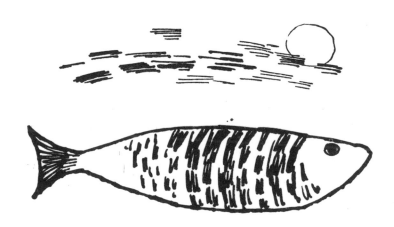

# Storms, Winds, Clouds

As the days lengthen,
So the storms strengthen.

No weather is ill
If the wind be still.

When clouds appear like rocks and towers
The earth's refreshed by frequent showers.

# Hee Haw

It is time to cock your hay and corn
When the old donkey blows his horn.

# The Leaves are Green

The leaves are green, the nuts are brown,
They hang so high they won't come down.
Leave them alone till frosty weather,
Then they will all come down together.

# A Sweet Country Life

A sweet country life is to me both dear and charming,
For to walk abroad on a fine summer's morning.

Your houses, your cities, your lofty gay towers
In nothing can compare with the sweet shady bowers.

Oh little do I admire your robes and fine dresses,
Your silks and your scarlets, and other excesses.

For my own country clothing is to me more endearing
Than your pretty sweet mantle for my homespun wearing.

No fiddle, no flute, no oboe nor spinet
Can ever compare with the lark or the linnet.

# The Fair Maid

The fair maid who, the first of May,
Goes to the fields at break of day,
And washes in dew from the hawthorn tree
Will ever after handsome be.

# Pips in the Fire

If you love me, pop and fly:
If you hate me, lay and die.

# Hempseed

*(Girls used to sow hempseed on All Hallows Eve)*

Hempseed I set,
Hempseed I sow.
The young man that I love,
Come after me and mow.

# Go to Bed

Go to bed first—
A golden purse.

Go to bed second—
A golden pheasant.

Go to bed third—
A golden bird.

# Brill

At Brill on the hill
The wind blows shrill,
The cook no meat can dress;
At Stow-on-the-Wold
The wind blows cold—
I know no more than this.

# Nettles

Nettles grow in an angry bush,
An angry bush, an angry bush.
Nettles grow in an angry bush—
  With my Hi, Ho, Hum!

# One Bowl, One Bottle

# One Bowl, One Bottle

(*To be spoken in one breath as long as you can*)

My father he left me, just as he was able,
One bowl, one bottle, one label;
Two bowls, two bottles, two labels;
Three bowls, three bottles, three labels—
       *And so on.*

# Three Crooked Cripples

Three crooked cripples
Crept through Cripplegate,
And through Cripplegate
Crept three crooked cripples.

# Robert Rowley

Robert Rowley rolled a round roll round,
A round roll Robert Rowley rolled round.
Where rolled the round roll Robert Rowley rolled round?

# Two Legs

Two legs sat upon three legs
With one leg in his lap.
In comes four legs
And runs away with one leg.
Up jumps two legs,
Catches up three legs,
Throws it after four legs
And makes him bring back one leg.

*(A riddle to illustrate: one leg is a leg of mutton,
two legs is a man, three legs is a stool, and four legs
a dog.)*

# As Black as Ink

As black as ink and isn't ink,
As white as milk and isn't milk,
As soft as silk and isn't silk,
And hops about like a filly-foal.

(*A magpie*)

# How Many Birds?

The cuckoo and the gowk,
The laverock and the lark,
The twire-snipe, the weather-bleak—
    How many birds is that?

(*Three: the second in each pair is
another name for the first*)

# A House Full

A house full, a hole full,
You cannot catch a bowl full.

(*Smoke*)

# White Bird Featherless

White bird featherless
Flew from Paradise,
  Pitched on the castle wall.
Along came Lord Landless,
Took it up handless,
And rode away horseless
  To the King's white hall.

*(Snow and sun)*

# Thirty White Horses

Thirty white horses
Upon a red hill,
    Now they tramp,
    Now they champ,
Now they stand still.

(*Teeth and tongue*)

# In Marble Halls

In marble halls as white as milk,
Lined with a skin as soft as silk,
Within a fountain crystal-clear,
A golden apple doth appear.
No doors there are to this stronghold,
Yet thieves break in and steel the gold.

(*An egg*)

# One Eye

I have a little sister,
They call her Pretty Peep.
She wades in the waters,
Deep, deep, deep!
She climbs up the mountains,
High, high, high.
My poor little sister,
She has but one eye.

(*A star*)

# The Broad Water

A water there is I must pass,
A broader water never was;
And yet of all waters I ever did see,
To pass over with less jeopardy.

(*The dew*)

# Elder  Belder

# Elder Belder

Elder belder, limber lock,
Three wives in a clock
Sit and sing
And call a spring.

# When I was a Little Boy

When I was a little boy, I had but little wit.
It is some time ago, and I've no more yet,
Nor ever, ever shall, until that I die,
For the longer I live, the more fool am I.

# Hurly Burly

Hurly, burly, trumpet, trace,
The cow stands in the market-place.
Some goes far and some goes near,
But where shall this poor henchman steer?

# Hot Cockles

The wind blows east, the wind blows west,
The wind blows o'er the cuckoo's nest.
Where is this poor man to go?
Over yond cuckoo's hill I-o!

# An Apple for the King

An apple for the King
And a pear for the Queen,
And a good jump over the bowling green.

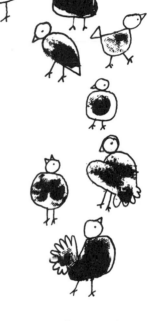

# The Poppet-Show

A pin to see the poppet-show,
A pin to see the poppet-show.
All manner of colours O,
See the ladies all below.

Black birds with blue feet
Walking up a new street,
One behind and one before
And one to knock at the barber's door.

# Blackthorn

Blackthorn, blackthorn,
Blue milk and barleycorn!
How many geese have you to-day?
More than you can carry away.

# I Doubt, I Doubt

I doubt, I doubt
My fire is out,
My little wife isn't at home.
I'll saddle my dog
An I'll bridle my cat,
And I'll go fetch my little wife home.

# Belle Isle

At the siege of Belle Isle
I was there all the while—
All the while, all the while
At the siege of Belle Isle.

# Brandy Hill

As I went up Brandy Hill
I met my father with good will.
He had jewels, he had rings,
He had many pretty things.
He'd a cat with nine tails,
He'd a hammer wanting nails.
Up Jock, down Tom!
Blow the bellows, old man.

# Little Boy

Little boy, little boy,
  Where wast thou born?
Far away in Lancashire
  Under a thorn,
Where they sup sour milk
  In a ram's horn.

# Tom Tinker's Ground

We are on Tom Tinker's ground
    Picking up gold and silver.
You pick weeds and I'll pick seeds
    And we'll pick caraway comfits.

# What's in There?

What's in there?
    Gold and money.
Where's my share of it?
    The mouse ran away with it.
Where's the mouse?
    In her house.

Where's the house?
    In the wood.
Where's the wood?
    The fire burnt it.
Where's the fire?
    The water quenched it.

Where's the water?
    The brown bull drank it.
Where's the brown bull?
    At the back of Birnie's Hill.
Where's Birnie's Hill?
    All clad with snow.
Where's the snow?
    The sun melted it.
Where's the sun?
    High, high up in the air.

# Hinx Minx

Hinx minx!
The old witch winks,
The fat begins to fry.
There's no one at home
But jumping Joan,
Father, mother, and I.

# The Hawthorn Tree

Green grow the leaves
   Upon the hawthorn tree.
Some they grow high
   And some they grow lee.
But the wranglers and the janglers,
   They never agree,
And the burden of my song
   Goes merrily.
Merrily, boys, merrily,
And the burden of my song
   Goes merrily.

# Up at Piccadilly O!

Up at Piccadilly O!
  The coachman takes his stand,
And when he meets a pretty girl
  He takes her by the hand.
Whip away for ever O!
Drive away so clever O!
All the way to Bristol O!
  He drives her four-in-hand.

# Little King Boggen

# Little King Boggen

Little King Boggen he built a fine hall,
Pie-crust and pastry-crust, that was the wall.
The windows were made of black-puddings and white,
And slated with pancakes—you ne'er saw the like.

# Barney Bodkin

Barney Bodkin broke his nose.
Without feet we can't have toes.
Crazy folks are always mad.
Want of money makes us sad.

# The Girl in the Lane

The girl in the lane
That couldn't speak plain
Cried 'Gobble, gobble, gobble'.
The man on the hill
That couldn't stand still
Went hobble, hobble, hobble.

# Isabella

Isabella, Isabella, Isabella, farewell.
    Last night when we parted
    I left you broken-hearted,
And on a green mountain there stands a young ma

The trees are uncovered, uncovered, uncovered,
The trees are uncovered, Isabella, for me.
    Last night when we parted
    I left you broken-hearted,
And on a green mountain there stands a young ma

# Myself

As I walked by myself
And talked to myself,
    Myself said unto me,
"Look to thyself,
Take care of thyself,
    For nobody cares for thee."

I answered myself,
And said to myself
    In the selfsame repartee,
"Look to thyself,
Or not look to thyself,
    The selfsame thing will be."

# Johnny Rover

I warn you once, I warn you twice,
I warn you three times over,
I warn you all to be witty and wise
And flee from Johnny Rover.

# Susie Mooney

Up the streets and down the streets,
    The windows made of glass—
Oh isn't Susie Mooney
    A pretty young lass?

# Mrs. Mason

Mrs. Mason
Broke a basin.
Mrs. Frost
Asked what it cost.
Mrs. Brown
Said, "Half-a-crown".
Mrs. Flory
Said, "What a story!"

# The Blacksmith

"Is John Smith within?"
"Yes, that he is."
"Can he set a shoe?"
"Aye, marry, two.
Here a nail and there a nail,
Tick, tack, too."

# I Had a Little Moppet

I had a little moppet
And put it in my pocket
    And fed it on corn and hay.
There came a proud beggar
And swore he would have her,
    And stole my poor moppet away.
And through the wild wood she ran, ran, ran,
And through the wild wood she ran;
And all the long winter
She followed the hunter
    And never was heard of again.

# One Misty Moisty Morning

One misty moisty morning
　　When cloudy was the weather,
There I met an old man
　　Clothed all in leather,
Clothed all in leather
　　With a cap beneath his chin—
"How do you do, and how do you do,
　　And how do you do again?"

# Moss

Moss was a little man
   And a little mare did buy,
For kicking and sprawling
   None her could come nigh.

She could trot, she could amble,
   And could canter here and there,
But one night she strayed away—
   So Moss lost his mare.

Moss got up next morning
 To catch her fast asleep,
And round about the frosty fields
 So nimbly he did creep.

Deep in a ditch he found her,
 And glad to find her there,
So I'll tell you by and by
 How Moss caught his mare.

"Rise, stupid, rise!"
 He thus to her did say.
"Arise, you beast, you drowsy beast,
 Get up without delay.

"For I must ride you to the town,
 So don't lie sleeping there."
He put the halter round her neck—
 So Moss caught his mare.

# Turvey

Turvey, Turvey, clothed in black
With silver buttons upon your back.
One by one and two by two,
Turn about and that will do.

# Old Abram Brown

Old Abram Brown is dead and gone,
You'll never see him more.
He used to wear a long brown coat
That buttoned down before.

# Cruel Tom

Who goes round my house this night?
   None but cruel Tom.
Who steals all the sheep at night?
   None but this poor one.

# Booman

Dill doule for Booman!
Booman is dead and gone,
Left his wife all alone
And all his children.

Where shall we bury him?
Carry him to London.
By his grandfather's grave
Grows a green onion.

Dig his grave wide and deep,
Strow it with flowers.
Toll the bell, toll the bell,
Twenty-four hours.

# Round Apples

Round apples, round apples
    By night and by day.
There stands a valley
    In yonder haze.
There stands poor Lizzie
    With a knife in her hand.
There's no one dare touch her
    Or she will go mad.
Her cheeks were like roses
    And now they're like snow.
Poor Lizzie, poor Lizzie,
    You're dying, I know.
We'll wash you with milk
    And we'll wrap you in silk
And we'll write down your name
    With a gold pen and ink.

# Hart and Hare

# Hart and Hare

The hart he loves the high wood,
    The hare she loves the hill.
The knight he loves his bright sword,
    The lady loves her will.

# Lady of the Land

Here's a poor widow from Babylon,
Six poor children left alone.
One can bake and one can brew
And one can shape and one can sew.
One can sit by the fire and spin,
And one can make a bed for a king.
Come Tuesday east, come Tuesday west,
Come choose the one that you love best.

# Anne

The wind blows high, the wind blows low,
The rain comes scattering down below.
Anne is handsome, Anne is pretty,
She is a girl of the golden city.
She goes courting one, two, three.
Please to tell me whose she'll be.

# Jacky's Fiddle

Jacky, come give me thy fiddle,
If ever thou mean to thrive.
Nay, I'll not give my fiddle
To any man alive.

If I should give my fiddle,
They'll think that I'm gone mad,
For many a joyful day
My fiddle and I have had.

# T'other Little Tune

I won't be my father's Jack,
  I won't be my mother's Jill.
I will be the fiddler's wife
  And have music when I will.
     T'other little tune,
     T'other little tune,
     Prithee, love, play me
     T'other little tune.

# Billy Taylor

Billy Taylor's a jolly sailor
    And shall be for ever more,
Went to sea and left his Sally
    Weeping on the Greenland shore.

I will buy you beads and ear-rings,
    I will buy you a diamond stone,
I will buy you a horse to ride on
    When your true love's dead and gone.

What care I for beads and ear-rings,
    What care I for the diamond stone,
What care I for a horse to ride on
    When my true love's dead and gone?

# Six Rows of Pins

"Madam, I present you with six rows of pins,
The very first offering my true love brings.
Madam, will you walk with me, me, me,
Oh madam, will you walk with me?"

"I will not accept of your six rows of pins,
The very first offering your true love brings,
And I won't walk with you, you, you,
And I won't walk with you."

"Madam, I present you with a little silver bell,
To call up your servants when you're not well.
Madam, will you walk with me, me, me,
Oh madam, will you walk with me?"

"I will not accept of your little silver bell,
To call up my servants when I'm not well,
And I won't walk with you, you, you,
And I won't walk with you."

"Madam, I present you with a pretty golden watch,
To hang by your side when you go to church.
Madam, will you walk with me, me, me,
Oh madam, will you walk with me?"

"I WILL accept of your little golden watch,
To hang by my side when I go to church,
And I WILL walk with you, you, you,
And I will walk with you."

# Trip Upon Trenchers

Trip upon trenchers, and dance upon dishes
   My mother sent me for some barm, some barm
She bid me tread lightly, and come again quickly
   For fear the young men should do me some ha:
Yet didn't you see, yet didn't you see
What naughty tricks they put upon me?
They broke my pitcher, and spilt the water,
And huffed my mother and chid her daughter,
And kissed my sister instead of me.

# Three Knights

"We are three knights come out of Spain
A-courting of your daughter Jane."
"My daughter Jane, she is too young,
She has not learned the Spanish tongue."
"Whether she be young or old,
She must have a gift of gold;
So fare you well, my lady gay,
We'll turn our heads another way."
"Come back, come back, thou Spanish knight,
And pick the fairest in your sight."

# The Birds of the Air

# The Birds of the Air

I went into the woods
  And built me a kirk,
And all the birds of the air
  They helped me to work.
The hawk with his long claws
  Pulled down the stone,
The dove with her rough bill
  Brought me them home.
The parrot was the clergyman,
  The peacock was the clerk,
The bullfinch played the organ,
  And we made merry work.

# There was a Pig

There was a pig
 Went out to dig
Christmas Day, Christmas Day,
 There was a pig
 Went out to dig
On Christmas Day in the mornir

There was a sow
 Went out to plough
Christmas Day, Christmas Day,
 There was a sow
 Went out to plough
On Christmas Day in the mornir

There was a sparrow
 Went out to harrow,
Christmas Day, Christmas Day,
 There was a sparrow
 Went out to harrow
On Christmas Day in the morni

There was a crow
Went out to sow,
Christmas Day, Christmas Day,
There was a crow
Went out to sow
On Christmas Day in the morning.

There was a sheep
Went out to reap,
Christmas Day, Christmas Day,
There was a sheep
Went out to reap
On Christmas Day in the morning.

# Cock Robin

Cock Robin got up early
  At the break of day
And went to Jenny's window
  To sing a roundelay.

He sang Cock Robin's love
  To the pretty Jenny Wren
And when he got unto the end
  Then he began again.

# Little Bob Robin

Little Bob Robin,
  Where do you live?

Up in yonder wood, sir,
  On a hazel twig.

# The Robin's Last Will

As I came past by Garrick
    And by the bridge of Dee,
I saw a little robin
    Sitting on a tree.

I said, "My pretty robin,
    How long have you sat here?"
He said, "I've lived upon this tree
    These four-and-twenty year."

"I'm going to make my testament
    Just here upon this tree,
I'm going to make my testament
    This day before I dee."

"I'll give my pretty head,
    It is both round and small,
Unto the boys of Garrick
    To play at the football."

"I'll give my pretty legs,
   They are both slim and tall,
Unto the bridge of Garrick:
   I hear it's going to fall."

As little robin ended
   He shut his pretty eyes,
And down he dropped unto the ground,
   Never more to rise.

# A Man of Words

A man of words and not of deeds
Is like a garden full of weeds,
And when the weeds begin to grow
It's like a garden full of snow,
And when the snow begins to fall
It's like a bird upon the wall,
And when the bird away does fly
It's like an eagle in the sky,
And when the sky begins to roar
It's like a lion at the door,
And when the door begins to crack
It's like a stick across your back,
And when your back begins to smart
It's like a penknife in your heart,
And when your heart begins to bleed
You're dead, and dead, and dead indeed.

# Jenny Wren Fell Sick

Jenny Wren fell sick
 Upon a merry time,
In came Robin Redbreast
 And brought her sops and wine.

"Eat well of the sop, Jenny,
 Drink well of the wine."
"Thank you, Robin, kindly,
 You shall be mine."

Jenny Wren got well,
 And stood upon her feet;
And told Robin quite plainly
 She loved him not a bit.

Robin he got angry
 And hopped upon a twig,
Saying, "Out upon you, fie upon you,
 Bold-faced jig!"

# The Cutty Wren

(Cutty *means* short-tailed *or* little. *It was an ancient custom in South Wales for two or four men to go about on St. Stephen's Day, December 26, carrying a wren fastened on two poles slung on their shoulders, groaning under its supposed weight and singing this song.*)

"Oh where are you going?" says Milder to Malder.
"Oh I cannot tell," says Festel to Fose.
"We're going to the woods," says John the Red Nose.

"Oh what will you do there?" says Milder to Malder.
"Oh I cannot tell," says Festel to Fose.
"We'll shoot the Cutty Wren," says John the Red Nose.

"Oh how will you shoot her?" says Milder to Malder.
"Oh I cannot tell," says Festal to Fose.
"With arrows and bows," says John the Red Nose.

117

"Oh that will not do," says Milder to Malder.
"Oh what will do then?" says Festel to Fose.
"With cannons and guns," says John the Red Nose.

"Oh how will you bring her home?" says Milder to Malder.
"Oh I cannot tell," says Festel to Fose.
"On four strong men's shoulders," says John the Red Nose.

"Oh that will not do," says Milder to Malder.
"Oh what will do then?" says Festel to Fose.
"In waggons and carts," says John the Red Nose.

"Oh what will you cut her up with?" says Milder to Malder.
"Oh I cannot tell," says Festel to Fose.
"With knives and with forks," says John the Red Nose.

"Oh that will not do," says Milder to Malder.
"Oh what will do then?" says Festel to Fose.
"With hatchets and cleavers," says John the Red Nose.

"Oh how will you boil her?" says Milder to Malder.
"Oh I cannot tell," says Festel to Fose.
"In kettles and pots," says John the Red Nose.

"Oh that will not do," says Milder to Malder.
"Oh what will do then?" says Festel to Fose.
"In cauldrons and pans," says John the Red Nose.

"Oh who'll have the spare ribs?" says Milder to Malder.
"Oh I cannot tell," says Festel to Fose.
"We'll give them to the poor," says John the Red Nose.

# Misty Moor

As I was going o'er misty moor
I spied three cats at a mill door.
One was white and one was black
And one was like my granny's cat.

I hopped over the stile and broke my heel,
I flew to Ireland very weel.
Spied an old woman sat by the fire
Sewing silk, jinking keys.

Cat's in the cream-pot up to her knees,
Hen's in the hurdle crowing for day.
Cock's in the barn threshing corn,
I never saw the like since I was born.

# The Thirteen Days

(Another version of *The Twelve Days of Christmas*. "Papingo-aye" means "peacock".)

The King sent his lady on the first Yule day
A papingo-aye.
Who learns my carol and carries it away?

The King sent his lady on the second Yule day
Three partridges, a papingo-aye.
Who learns my carol and carries it away?

The King sent his lady on the third Yule day
Three plovers, three partridges, and a papingo-aye . . .
*(and so on)*

The King sent his lady on the fourth Yule day
A goose that was grey,
Three plovers . . .
*(and so on)*

The King sent his lady on the fifth Yule day
Three starlings, a goose that was grey . . .
*(and so on)*

The King sent his lady on the sixth Yule day
Three goldspinks, three starlings . . .
*(and so on)*

The King sent his lady on the seventh Yule day
A bull that was brown, three goldspinks . . .
*(and so on)*

The King sent his lady on the eighth Yule day
Three ducks a-merry laying, a bull that was brown . . .

*(and so on)*

The King sent his lady on the ninth Yule day
Three swans a-merry swimming, three ducks a-merry laying . . .

*(and so on)*

The King sent his lady on the tenth Yule day
An Arabian baboon, three swans a-merry swimming . . .

*(and so on)*

The King sent his lady on the eleventh Yule day
Three hinds a-merry hunting, an Arabian baboon . . .

(and so on)

The King sent his lady on the twelfth Yule day
Three maids a-merry dancing, three hinds a-merry hunting . . .

(and so on)

The King sent his lady on the thirteenth Yule day
Three stalks o'merry corn, three maids a-merry dancing . . .

(and so on)

# Children's Books by James Reeves

## THE CHRISTMAS BOOK
### Illustrated by Raymond Briggs

A feast of stories, poems, carols, relating to the twelve days of Christmas, chosen with James Reeves' inspired touch.

## RAGGED ROBIN
### Illustrated by Jane Paton

A poem and a full colour picture for every letter of the alphabet. "True poetry, and the illustrations are so much in sympathy that they are as leaves from the same tree"
—*New Statesman*

## THE WANDERING MOON
### Illustrated by Edward Ardizzone

Poems. "His fancy, reflection and narrative move with graceful freedom"—*The Times Literary Supplement*

## PREFABULOUS ANIMILES
### Illustrated by Edward Ardizzone

"Author and artist are awarded a double first"
—*The Times Literary Supplement*

## SAILOR RUMBELOW AND BRITANNIA
### Illustrated by Edward Ardizzone

"Prose and pictures interact to produce a perfect fairytale world"—*The Listener*

## PIGEONS AND PRINCESSES
### Illustrated by Edward Ardizzone

"In the purest tradition of the fairytale . . . the very stuff of children's literature"—*Junior Bookshelf*